THE ENGLISH RUNES

RUNE OF THE DAY JOURNAL

Suzanne Rance

Dragon House

First Printed 2017

Published by
Dragon House

Copyright © 2017 Suzanne Rance

Cover Art © 2017 Emma Martin

suzanne@suzannerance.co.uk
www.suzannerance.co.uk

ISBN 978 0 9957264 2 0

How to use this Rune of the Day Journal

This rune of the day journal is designed as a companion to The English Runes *Secrets of Magic, Spells and Divination.*

It has been created to enable you to choose one rune of the day and/or a three rune spread. Here you can record your thoughts on the runes you draw, however often; this practice will enable you to build your divinatory skills and deepen your knowledge and understanding.

My hope is that this journal will become an invaluable resource and revisiting your own thoughts and explorations will help you become an expert practitioner.

Remember it is your own personal connection to each individual rune and the magic that surrounds it that brings the runes to life and makes them sing.

Suzanne Rance
Sussex, England
Spring 2017

Date: _____ / _____ / _____

Rune of the Day	Meanings

Three Rune Spread

Rune 1	Rune 2	Rune 3

Observations on spread

Notes

Date:_____/_____/_____

Rune of the Day	Meanings

Three Rune Spread

Rune 1	Rune 2	Rune 3

Observations on spread

Notes

Date:_____/_____/_____

Rune of the Day	Meanings

Three Rune Spread

Rune 1	Rune 2	Rune 3

Observations on spread

Notes

Date: _____ / _____ / _____

Rune of the Day	Meanings

Three Rune Spread

Rune 1	Rune 2	Rune 3

Observations on spread

Notes

Date: _____/_____/_____

Rune of the Day	Meanings

Three Rune Spread

Rune 1	Rune 2	Rune 3

Observations on spread

Notes

Date:_____/_____/_____

Rune of the Day	Meanings

Three Rune Spread

Rune 1	Rune 2	Rune 3

Observations on spread

Notes

Date:_____/_____/_____

Rune of the Day	Meanings

Three Rune Spread

Rune 1	Rune 2	Rune 3

Observations on spread

Notes

Date:_____/_____/_____

Rune of the Day	Meanings

Three Rune Spread

Rune 1	Rune 2	Rune 3

Observations on spread

Notes

Date:_____/_____/_____

Rune of the Day	Meanings

Three Rune Spread

Rune 1	Rune 2	Rune 3

Observations on spread

Notes

Date:_____/_____/_____

Rune of the Day	Meanings

Three Rune Spread

Rune 1	Rune 2	Rune 3

Observations on spread

Notes

Date:_____/_____/_____

Rune of the Day	Meanings

Three Rune Spread

Rune 1	Rune 2	Rune 3

Observations on spread

Notes

Date:_____ /_____ /_____

Rune of the Day	Meanings

Three Rune Spread

Rune 1	Rune 2	Rune 3

Observations on spread

Notes

Date:_____/_____/_____

Rune of the Day	Meanings

Three Rune Spread

Rune 1	Rune 2	Rune 3

Observations on spread

Notes

Date:_____/_____/_____

Rune of the Day	Meanings

Three Rune Spread

Rune 1	Rune 2	Rune 3

Observations on spread

Notes

Date:_____/_____/_____

Rune of the Day	Meanings

Three Rune Spread

Rune 1	Rune 2	Rune 3

Observations on spread

Notes

Date:_____/_____/_____

Rune of the Day	Meanings

Three Rune Spread

Rune 1	Rune 2	Rune 3

Observations on spread

Notes

Date: _____ / _____ / _____

Rune of the Day	Meanings

Three Rune Spread

Rune 1	Rune 2	Rune 3

Observations on spread

Notes

Date:_____/_____/_____

Rune of the Day	Meanings

Three Rune Spread

Rune 1	Rune 2	Rune 3

Observations on spread

Notes

Date:_____/_____/_____

Rune of the Day	Meanings

Three Rune Spread

Rune 1	Rune 2	Rune 3

Observations on spread

Notes

Date:_____/_____/_____

Rune of the Day	Meanings

Three Rune Spread

Rune 1	Rune 2	Rune 3

Observations on spread

Notes

Date:_____/_____/_____

Rune of the Day	Meanings

Three Rune Spread

Rune 1	Rune 2	Rune 3

Observations on spread

Notes

Date:_____/_____/_____

Rune of the Day	Meanings

Three Rune Spread

Rune 1	Rune 2	Rune 3

Observations on spread

Notes

Date:_____/_____/_____

Rune of the Day	Meanings

Three Rune Spread

Rune 1	Rune 2	Rune 3

Observations on spread

Notes

Date:_____/_____/_____

Rune of the Day	Meanings

Three Rune Spread

Rune 1	Rune 2	Rune 3

Observations on spread

Notes

Date:_____/_____/_____

Rune of the Day	Meanings

Three Rune Spread

Rune 1	Rune 2	Rune 3

Observations on spread

Notes

Date:_____/_____/_____

Rune of the Day	Meanings

Three Rune Spread

Rune 1	Rune 2	Rune 3

Observations on spread

Notes

Date:_____/_____/_____

Rune of the Day	Meanings

Three Rune Spread

Rune 1	Rune 2	Rune 3

Observations on spread

Notes

Date: _____ / _____ / _____

Rune of the Day	Meanings

Three Rune Spread

Rune 1	Rune 2	Rune 3

Observations on spread

Notes

Date:_____/_____/_____

Rune of the Day	Meanings

Three Rune Spread

Rune 1	Rune 2	Rune 3

Observations on spread

Notes

Date:____/____/____

Rune of the Day	Meanings

Three Rune Spread

Rune 1	Rune 2	Rune 3

Observations on spread

Notes

Date:_____/_____/_____

Rune of the Day	Meanings

Three Rune Spread

Rune 1	Rune 2	Rune 3

Observations on spread

Notes

Date:_____/_____/_____

Rune of the Day	Meanings

Three Rune Spread

Rune 1	Rune 2	Rune 3

Observations on spread

_____

_____

_____

_____

Notes

_____

_____

_____

_____

Date:_____/_____/_____

Rune of the Day | Meanings

Three Rune Spread

Rune 1	Rune 2	Rune 3

Observations on spread

Notes

Date:_____/_____/_____

Rune of the Day	Meanings

Three Rune Spread

Rune 1	Rune 2	Rune 3

Observations on spread

Notes

Date:_____/_____/_____

Rune of the Day	Meanings

Three Rune Spread

Rune 1	Rune 2	Rune 3

Observations on spread

Notes

Date:_____/_____/_____

Rune of the Day	Meanings

Three Rune Spread

Rune 1	Rune 2	Rune 3

Observations on spread

_____

_____

_____

_____

Notes

_____

_____

_____

_____

Date:_____/_____/_____

Rune of the Day	Meanings

Three Rune Spread

Rune 1	Rune 2	Rune 3

Observations on spread

Notes

Date:_____/_____/_____

Rune of the Day	Meanings

Three Rune Spread

Rune 1	Rune 2	Rune 3

Observations on spread

Notes

Date:_____ / _____ / _____

Rune of the Day	Meanings

Three Rune Spread

Rune 1	Rune 2	Rune 3

Observations on spread

Notes

Date:_____/_____/_____

Rune of the Day	Meanings

Three Rune Spread

Rune 1	Rune 2	Rune 3

Observations on spread

Notes

Date:_____/_____/_____

Rune of the Day | Meanings

Rune of the Day	Meanings

Three Rune Spread

Rune 1	Rune 2	Rune 3

Observations on spread

Notes

Date:_____/_____/_____

Rune of the Day	Meanings

Three Rune Spread

Rune 1	Rune 2	Rune 3

Observations on spread

Notes

Date:____/____/____

Rune of the Day	Meanings

Three Rune Spread

Rune 1	Rune 2	Rune 3

Observations on spread

Notes

Date:_____ / _____ / _____

Rune of the Day	Meanings

Three Rune Spread

Rune 1	Rune 2	Rune 3

Observations on spread

_____

_____

_____

_____

Notes

_____

_____

_____

_____

Date:_____/_____/_____

Rune of the Day	Meanings

Three Rune Spread

Rune 1	Rune 2	Rune 3

Observations on spread

Notes

Date:_____/_____/_____

Rune of the Day	Meanings

Three Rune Spread

Rune 1	Rune 2	Rune 3

Observations on spread

Notes

Date:_____/_____/_____

Rune of the Day	Meaning

Three Rune Spread

Rune 1	Rune 2	Rune 3

Observations on spread

_____

_____

_____

_____

Notes

_____

_____

_____

_____

_____

Date:_____/_____/_____

Rune of the Day	Meaning

Three Rune Spread

Rune 1	Rune 2	Rune 3

Observations on spread

Notes

Date:_____/_____/_____

Rune of the Day	Meaning

Three Rune Spread

Rune 1	Rune 2	Rune 3

Observations on spread

Notes

Date:_____/_____/_____

Rune of the Day	Meaning

Three Rune Spread

Rune 1	Rune 2	Rune 3

Observations on spread

Notes

Date:_____/_____/_____

Rune of the Day	Meaning

Three Rune Spread

Rune 1	Rune 2	Rune 3

Observations on spread

Notes

Date:_____/_____/_____

Rune of the Day	Meaning

Three Rune Spread

Rune 1	Rune 2	Rune 3

Observations on spread

Notes

Date:_____ / _____ / _____

Rune of the Day	Meaning

Three Rune Spread

Rune 1	Rune 2	Rune 3

Observations on spread

Notes

Date:_____/_____/_____

Rune of the Day	Meaning

Three Rune Spread

Rune 1	Rune 2	Rune 3

Observations on spread

Notes

Date:_____/_____/_____

Rune of the Day	Meaning

Three Rune Spread

Rune 1	Rune 2	Rune 3

Observations on spread

_____

_____

_____

_____

Notes

_____

_____

_____

_____

_____

Date:_____/_____/_____

Rune of the Day	Meaning

Three Rune Spread

Rune 1	Rune 2	Rune 3

Observations on spread

Notes

Date:_____/_____/_____

Rune of the Day	Meaning

Three Rune Spread

Rune 1	Rune 2	Rune 3

Observations on spread

Notes

Date:_____/_____/_____

Rune of the Day	Meaning

Three Rune Spread

Rune 1	Rune 2	Rune 3

Observations on spread

Notes

Date:_____/_____/_____

Rune of the Day	Meaning

Three Rune Spread

Rune 1	Rune 2	Rune 3

Observations on spread

_____

_____

_____

_____

Notes

_____

_____

_____

_____

_____

Date:_____ / _____ / _____

Rune of the Day	Meaning

Three Rune Spread

Rune 1	Rune 2	Rune 3

Observations on spread

Notes

Rune Table

Rune	Letter	Basic divination meanings and ide
ᚠ Feoh Wealth	*f*	Money, Generosity | Comfort | Sharing money or skills | Things that can be sold to raise money | Skills you have that can be exchanged for money
ᚢ Ūr Aurochs	*u*	Strength, bodily or mental | Proud and Brave | Initiation | Rite of Passage | Independent | Courageous | Worthy of joining the club | Adulthood
ᚦ Thorn Thurs	*þ, ð, th*	Sharp | Causing pain and discomfort | Menstrual pain, women's problems, heavy blood loss, peri-menopausal symptoms | Being attacked | Giant | Defence, of friends, family, property
ᚩ Ōs God Woden	*o*	Wisdom |Prophetic speech | Common sense | Source of comfort through understanding and insight | Woden as the wise one | Healing | Frenzy | Confidence
ᚱ Rād Riding	*r*	Travel, road, pathway |Mode of transpor car, motorbike etc | Furniture/seating on the transport and in the home | Pride of ownership | Boasting

Rune	Letter	Basic divination meanings and idea
ᚳ Cēn Torch	c	Bright light | Clarity | Knowledge | Information gained through discussion with others | Keen, brave, bold | Conceive, create
ᚷ Gyfu Gift	g	Giving and receiving | Conditional vs unconditional | Gratitude | Relationship Responsibility | Honour and reputation
ᚹ Wen Happiness	w	Joy, bliss | Recognition and understanding of a happy state | Lack of poverty | Ability to rise out of the depths | People who support you | Friends and family you can trust
ᚻ Hægl Hail	h	Something temptingly beautiful that disappears | Sudden devastation | A promise that turns to nothing | Look beneath the surface | Beware a con
ᚾ Nȳd Need	n	Necessity, obligation, service | The gut feeling of need or want | Recognised early it can be lessened or understood | A shaper of Wyrd

Rune	Letter	Basic divination meanings and ide
Ꮁ Īs Ice	i	Frozen, extreme cold | Slippery and dangerous | Difficult to negotiate | Beauty or temptation, best viewed from a place of safety | Slow moving | Appears stuck
⟡ Gēr Harvest	j	Year, end of the year | A blessing or good outcome | Planning for the next season/year | Decisions to be made, may be difficult
⌐ Ēoh Yew	eo	A fire keeper, Slow burning |Unsmooth and ancient | Everlasting |Connection to ancestors | Important part of your homeland or place you love
⚶ Peorð Gaming	p	Companionship |Pleasure and laughter | Gamble | Life on the edge | Sudden change | A doorway to another realm | Liminal space
Ψ Eolhx Elk	x	Independent, Protective, Adaptable | Will fight if cornered | Wounds | Divine Twins | Grove, Sanctuary |Cross dressing Shape changing | Gender dysphoria or fluidity

Rune	Letter	Basic divination meanings and idea
ᛋ Sigel Sun	s	Navigation | Guidance during daylight | Safety | Overseas travel | Positive signs and indications
ᛏ Tīr Tiw, a God	t	A sign that holds true | Guidance after dark | The pole star |A God of War and Judgement | Luck in battle | Connection with ancestors | The Green Man
ᛒ Beorc Birch	b	Beginning , Pioneering, Adaptable, Nurturing | Spring | Fire | Tall and beautiful |Family connections | Communications, through roots and as paper |Fire starter, water holder, container
ᛗ Eh Horse	e	Sovereignty | Freedom |Restless spirit | Help in carrying loads, people, goods, burdens
ᛘ Man Mankind	m	Friendship | Love | Relationship | Security of community | Fallibility | Can only be relied upon in the short term

Rune	Letter	Basic divination meanings and ide
ᛚ Lagu Water	*l*	Large body of water | Emotions | Rules | Law | If you don't follow the rules then you will come unstuck | Control of emotions and your destiny
ᛝ Ing A God, Frea	ŋ	Fertility and Family ties | A fertile field | Blessings of the Earth Mother | A journey Eastward | Pilgrimage | Peace | Banishing of weapons
ᛟ Ēðel Homeland	œ	Inheritance | Family land |Tribal land | The place you feel most at home | Place you yearn for | Spirits of your place of connection
ᛞ Dæg Day	*d*	Daylight | A working day | Productive time | See things clearly | Shines light in the dark places| Chases the monsters away
ᚪ Āc Oak	*a*	Strength | Endurance | A national symbol | Free foods for animals | Forests | Autumn | Acorns | Boats | A world tree | Thunor or Thor

Rune	Letter	Basic divination meanings and ide
Æsc Ash	œ	World Tree Yggdrasil | Strong, tall, straight | Protective against force | Fuel for warmth, burns green | A primal being | Creation story ancestor
ȳr Yew bow	y	Skill | The very best equipment | Attractive accessory | Fighting force | Surprise attack | Overwhelming
Īar Beaver	ia, io	Home building | Place of safety | Comfortable abode | Good food | Hard work, with results | Determination
Ēar Grave	ea	Death | All things must end | Sacrifice | John Barley Corn | An ear of corn | The cycle of life | End of one life cycle